ROD SERLING's

THE TWILIGHT ZONE

WILL THE REAL MARTIAN
PLEASE STAND UP?

Adaptation from Rod Serling's original script by

MARK KNEECE

Illustrated by

RICH ELLIS

BLOOMSBURY

LONDON BERLIN NEW YORK

INTRODUCTION

There is a fifth dimension beyond that which is known to man. It is a dimension as vast as space and timeless as infinity. It is the middle ground between light and shadow, between science and superstition, and it lies between the pit of man's fears and the summit of his knowledge. This is the dimension of imagination. It is an area which we call the Twilight Zone.

America, between the 1950s and early 1960s, was itself in a sort of "twilight zone." Following the victories of World War II and the attending economic boom—but before the Civil Rights marches; the assassinations of John F. Kennedy, Martin Luther King, Jr., and Robert F. Kennedy; and the Vietnam War—we were wrapped in a gleaming package of shining chrome, white picket fences, and Hollywood glamour. But beneath this shimmering facade lay a turbulent core of racial inequality, sexual inequality, and the Cold War threat of nuclear attacks from the Soviet Union. We'd never been more affluent—or more frightened.

Enter Rodman Edward Serling of Binghamton, New York. Serling began writing in his teens for his high school newspaper; as a student at Antioch College, he was already selling scripts to radio programs. While serving as a paratrooper in the U.S. Army Eleventh Airborne (for which he earned a Purple Heart), he wrote for the Armed Services Radio. He went on to write for film and television, first in feature presentations for *Hallmark Hall of Fame* and *Playhouse 90*, including the lauded "Requiem for a Heavyweight," perhaps drawing inspiration from his own experiences as a Golden Gloves boxer. More than two hundred of his teleplays were produced. In all, his work would win not only the adoration of listeners and viewers but a host of prestigious awards, including a record-breaking six Emmy awards—two of them for his greatest achievement, *The Twilight Zone*.

The worlds and characters presented over the course of five seasons, beginning in October 1959, were like nothing audiences had seen before. Television, the new "must have" appliance for America's increasingly prosperous households, offered comedies such as *I Love Lucy* and *The Honeymooners*, news programs including Edward R. Murrow's *See It Now*, as well as Westerns, game shows, and soap operas. With a typewriter as his spade, Serling dug beneath the surface of the expected and planted the seeds of a more imaginative and thoughtful genre, writing more than half of the show's 156 episodes while producing and hosting all of them. He bravely took on themes of oppression, prejudice, and paranoia, all the while giving people what they needed at the end of the day: entertainment.

While he had his run-ins with censorship, Serling's clever use of other worlds and veiled scenarios generally protected him. As he explained, what he couldn't have a Republican or a Democrat espouse on the show, he could have an alien profess without offending the sponsors. This approach also allowed viewers to take away whatever message best suited them; the more reflective could consider the psychological and political implications, while others might be satisfied with simply enjoying the thrill of the surface story. So much more than mere science fiction or fantasy, Serling's scripts are parables that explore the multifaceted natures of hope, fear, humanity, loneliness, and self-delusion.

Half a century later, *The Twilight Zone* remains a part of our culture, routinely referenced in print and on television, having become a shorthand expression that succinctly describes the bizarre and unexpected. The original episodes are still aired on the SciFi Channel, both in late-night slots and as day-long marathons. The show was literally a Who's Who of Hollywood, helping to foster the careers of fledgling actors including Robert Redford, Ron Howard, Dennis Hopper, Charles Bronson, and William Shatner. It has also inspired countless authors and filmmakers, who have gone on to break through boundaries of their own.

In the fifty years since *The Twilight Zone* first aired, we've faced new enemies and have altered our definitions of happiness, but our core hopes and fears remain the same, as does our desire to be entertained. The stories are as compelling, and as telling, as ever. And now, in their newest incarnation, Serling's scripts serve as the basis for this graphic novel series, which honors the original text and even echoes the storyboarding of television, but offers a fresh interpretation, as seen through the eyes of a new generation of artists.

—Anna Marlis Burgard
Director of Industry Partnerships, Savannah College of Art and Design

You're traveling through
another dimension,
a dimension not only of sight and sound
but of mind;
a journey into a wondrous land
whose boundaries
are that of imagination.
That's the signpost up ahead—
your next stop,
the Twilight Zone!

SEE ANYTHING?

TREES. SNOW. THAT'S ABOUT IT.

JUST A SEC!

PUT THE LIGHT OVER THERE.

THAT'S PRECIOUS LITTLE CONSOLATION FOR MISSING MY MEETING IN BOSTON!

YOU WORK FOR QUITE A BUS LINE.

THEY DON'T CARE MUCH ABOUT A SCHEDULE, DO THEY?

DON'T BE SO HARD ON THE BUS LINE, MISTER.

THEY DON'T CONTROL THE SNOWFALL, THE SORRY-BUILT BRIDGES, OR THE SIDES OF HILLS THAT DECIDE TO COME DOWN.

THAT'S ALL PRETTY MUCH OUT OF THEIR HANDS.

munch munch munch

OH, THIS IS RICH!

BETTER'N A HORROR MOVIE. SHE DON'T KNOW WHO HE IS, AND HE DON'T KNOW WHO SHE IS. HA HA HA!

HEY, DON'T LET HER TOUCH YOU NOW! WE DON'T KNOW WHO SHE IS OR WHERE SHE'S BEEN.

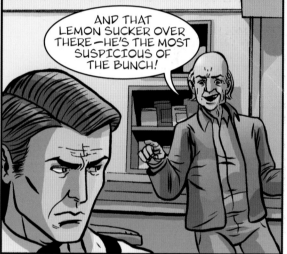

AND THAT LEMON SUCKER OVER THERE—HE'S THE MOST SUSPICIOUS OF THE BUNCH!

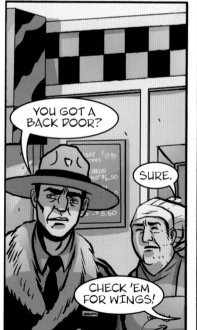

YOU GOT A BACK DOOR?

SURE.

CHECK 'EM FOR WINGS!

IS IT LOCKED?

YEAH. I THINK SO, ANYWAY. MAYBE.

LOOK UNDER THEIR COATS!

GO BACK THERE AND MAKE SURE, WILL YA?

CHECK 'EM ALL FOR WINGS!

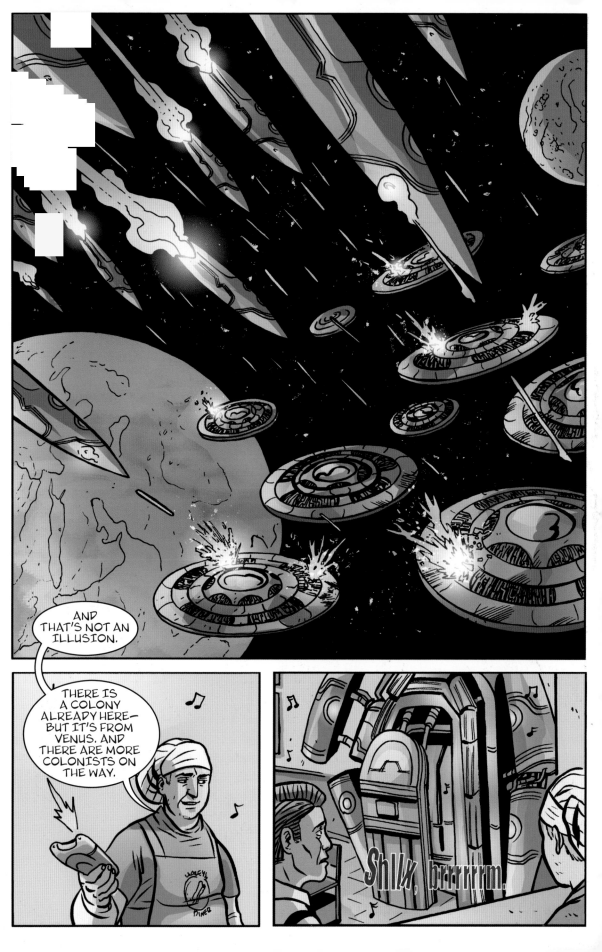

Will the Real Martian Please Stand Up?

Season Two, Episode #28

Original Air Date: May 26, 1961

Written by Rod Serling

Cast

Narrator: Rod Serling

Ross: John Hoyt*
*Also appeared in *The Lateness of the Hour* as Dr. William Loren

Ethel McConnell: Jean Willes

Avery: Jack Elam

Haley, the Bartender: Barney Phillips*
*Also appeared in *Miniature* as Diemel
A Thing About Machines as TV Repairman
The Purple Testament as Capt. E. L. Gunther

Trooper Bill Padgett: John Archer

Olmstead, the Bus Driver: William Kendis (as Bill Kendis)*
*Also appeared in *The Fever* as Public Relations Man

Trooper Dan Perry: Morgan Jones*
*Also appeared in *The Parallel* as Captain

Rose Kramer: Gertrude Flynn

Peter Kramer: Bill Erwin*
*Also appeared in *Mute* as Man in Flashback (uncredited)
Mr. Denton on Doomsday as Man

Connie Prince: Jill Ellis

George Prince: Ron Kipling

Crew

Producer: Buck Houghton

Director: Montgomery Pittman

Director of Photography: George T. Clemens

Film Editor: Leon Barsha

Production Note

When Serling wrote the story outline for this episode, it originally featured a dog as the Martian. By airtime, the Martian had taken human form, presenting Serling and his technical crew with a challenge—how to give the alien a third arm. The low-tech answer was to have a crew member hide under the actor's overcoat and slide out his arm from underneath, with a matching shirt and highly choreographed motions. The higher-tech special effect was the Venusian third eye, which took days to construct, troubleshoot, and match to the actor's face. Ironically, to a modern viewer it is the extra eye that is remembered as the cheesy special effect, while the low-tech third arm continues to surprise and delight.

ADAPTING STORIES FROM ROD SERLING'S
THE TWILIGHT ZONE

In terms of screenwriting adaptations it's trying to cut out stuff that's extraneous, without doing damage to the original piece, because you owe a debt of some respect to the original author.

—Rod Serling, 1975

At first, the idea sounded straightforward. Take an original *Twilight Zone* screenplay and adapt it into a graphic novel—break the visuals into panels, move the dialogue into balloons and captions. After all, Rod Serling himself was a fan of comics, and graphic novels are their visual and literary heirs. Serling collected Entertaining Comics titles such as *Tales from the Crypt* and *Weird Science*, the themes of which resonate in *The Twilight Zone*; even Serling's trademark narration could be considered an echo of the Crypt Keeper's introductions. Yet the more I considered the task of adapting the scripts, the more the gravity of what I was doing set in. I grew up watching *The Twilight Zone*, after all, as did so many Americans. The work required a certain reverential perspective, considering the show's iconic status, not to mention the quality of the original material.

In the 1950s the comics Serling had enjoyed were considered subversive, a threat to America's youth. Frederick Wertham published *Seduction of the Innocent* in 1954, excoriating comics in an atmosphere of public paranoia similar to a scene from *The Monsters Are Due on Maple Street*. A year later, a Senate committee was convened to investigate the pernicious influence of horror comics on America's youth, and the Comics Code Authority was established to censor comics' content. EC Comics went out of business as a direct result. In an interesting twist of fate, by the end of the decade *The Twilight Zone* was just beginning to find its television audience with stories that probably would not have made it past the comics censors. Recreating Serling's stories now, in graphic novel form, seems appropriate, emblematic of an era in which comics are finding a new readership, achieving new respect, and speaking to a new audience receptive to a more sophisticated message.

Serling's stories run the gamut from serious drama, filled with fantastic and frightening dilemmas of the human condition, to wry, tongue-in-cheek humor in a sci-fi wrapper. Selecting eight as graphic novel material meant making difficult choices. Serling was a prolific writer, creating more than half of *The Twilight Zone*'s 156 scripts. It was not only a question of which of these would work best in novelized format, but which ones, as a group, would come closest to capturing the essence of *The Twilight Zone*. The stories ultimately chosen for these books possess the strongest visual possibilities and reflect an effort to achieve a cross section of Serling's dramatic range.

As I began adapting the stories for artists, I immersed myself in the screenplays and watched each episode until I felt I had internalized not just the characters, the plot, and the point, but what I imagined to be something of the author himself. In the process, I felt a growing kinship with Serling. Parts of the screenplay were often deleted from the actual show. Lines, characters, even entire scenes were struck, sometimes for budgetary reasons, sometimes because of time constraints, sometimes perhaps because Serling himself may have anticipated problems with the scenes. The show usually had only a thirty-minute time slot. The deleted scenes, however, often add richness and complexity to the story, offering a glimmer into what Serling might have done were it not for the constraints of the television medium. Restoring scenes seemed to help push the story even harder. I felt as if I were developing Serling's original design, following the telling to its logical conclusion.

With each of these stories, I have aspired to take advantage of what the graphic novel format can do. Art and text draw the reader deeply into the narrative. The reader does not just hear, but ponders, actively bridging the gaps between the panels of art with his or her own imagination. The story doesn't just happen to the reader, but, in part, *is* the reader. In other words, *The Twilight Zone* episodes had to be recreated not just to fit into a graphic novel format but to belong to it.

As much as possible, I have endeavored to keep the intentions of the original story intact—that is the "debt of respect" owed to Serling—fully functional in a new medium. From some nearby fifth dimension, I hope Serling is smiling at the prospect of these books, pleased at the thought of a new generation arriving by way of a different avenue perhaps, but entering and being welcomed into the fold of "Zonies" around the world.

—Mark Kneece
Professor of Sequential Art, Savannah College of Art and Design

Acknowledgments

Our thanks go to Carol Serling for her time and consideration while reviewing the adaptation
texts and illustrated pages, and also to John Lowe, chair of the Sequential Art Department at Savannah
College of Art and Design, for his assistance in pairing the right artists with the right stories.

Bloomsbury Publishing, London, Berlin and New York

First published in Great Britain in 2009 by Bloomsbury Publishing Plc
36 Soho Square, London, W1D 3QY

First published in the USA in 2009 by Walker & Company
175 Fifth Avenue, New York, NY 10010

Packaged by Design Press, a division of Savannah College of Art and Design, Inc.*
22 East Lathrop Street, Savannah, Georgia 31415, USA

Adaptation from Rod Serling's original script by Mark Kneece
Illustrated by Rich Ellis
Lettering by Thomas Zielonka
Series title treatment by Devin O'Bryan
Series copyediting by Kerri O'Hern
Series creative development by Anna Marlis Burgard and Emily Easton
Series art direction and design by Angela Rojas
Series project management by Angela Rojas and Melissa Kavonic
Creative consultant: Carol Serling

Photograph of Rod Serling © Bettmann/Corbis

A CIP catalogue record of this book is available from the British Library

ISBN 978 0 7475 8782 8

Printed in China by C & C Offset

1 3 5 7 9 10 8 6 4 2

All papers used by Bloomsbury Publishing are natural, recyclable products made from wood grown in well-managed forests.
The manufacturing processes conform to the environmental regulations of the country of origin

www.bloomsbury.com/childrens
The Savannah College of Art and Design: www.scad.edu